SCOOBY SNACKS

£7.99

D0493148

WELCOME

THIS ANNUAL BELONGS TO:

....

MINI MYSTERY

There are **10** hidden werewolf footprints in this Annual that could be vital clues. Help find them and list the page numbers below.

Contents

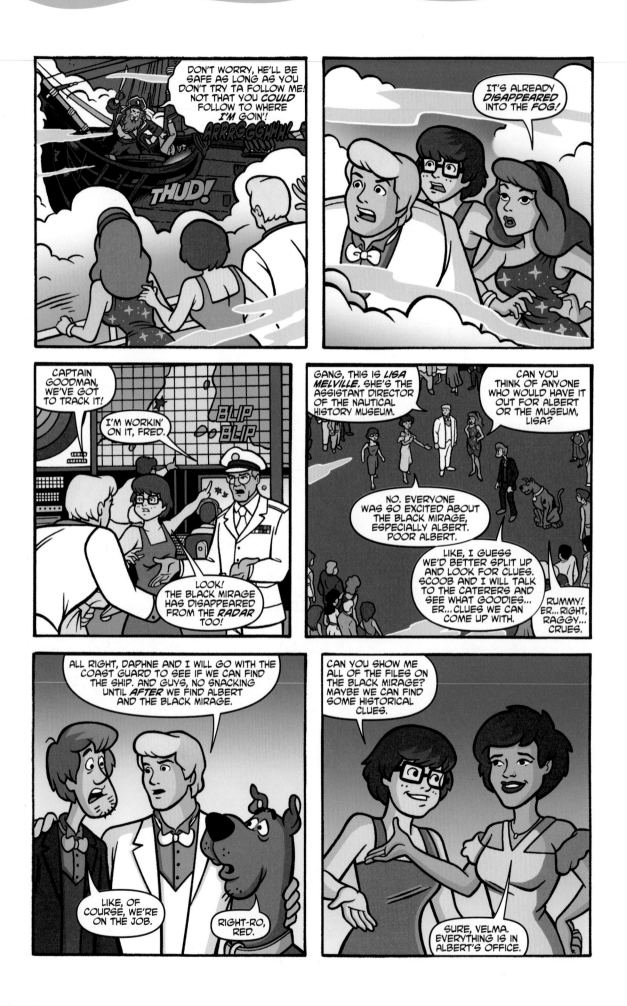

CONTINUED ON PAGE 12

9

Groovy Doodles!

1 Start by drawing a sausage shape for his body and a circle for his head. Sketch in the position of his chin.

2 Draw some long curved lines for his legs and sketch in his shoes. Draw two lines for the position of his arms and sausages for his hands. Now draw in Shaggy's mop of hair.

3 Draw in Shaggy's t-shirt and complete his arms and hands. Add the details to his shoes.

4 Add the details to Shaggy's face, including the whiskers on his chin. Don't forget to add in his knobbly knees. Once you are happy with your drawing, go over it with a pen and rub out any unwanted lines.

Funny Face!

Start with a circle for his head and a smaller semi-circle for the chin area.

Sketch in his crazy mop of hair and add in his eyes, nose and a big smile.

Now try drawing your own picture of Shaggy in the space below.

SECRET STORAGE!

This portrait has got lots of hidden features. The eyes can move and it has a secret storage section, perfect for stashing all your secret documents!

You will need:

Card,
a large flat cardboard box,
scissors,
PVA glue,
newspaper,
paints and
a paintbrush,
rhinestones,
sticky tape.

Jinkies! I think that portrait is keeping an eye on me!

1

Cut a slot in the top of the large cardboard box.
Paint the box black and leave it to dry.

2

Cut a piece of card the same size as the cardboard box.
Cover it with two layers of papier maché and leave it to dry.

3

Cut a larger rectangle of card and cut a hole in
the middle to make the frame. Trim the edges to make
the frame more ornate. Cover this with a layer of
papier maché. Once it is dry you can paint it.

4

Draw a portrait of a person in the centre of the
card rectangle. Cut holes where the eyes should go.
Paint the portrait and once it is dry, glue the
frame into place.

5

Cut a long strip of white card. Paint two black dots onto it.
Lay it onto the back of the portrait in the right place and
use sticky tape to fix two pieces of card over it. Only glue
the ends of the card strips so that the long strip can slide
back and forth, allowing the eyes to move.

6

Glue the portrait onto the front of the black box.
Decorate it with the rhinestone or glitter.
Hang it on the wall and store secret documents
in the slot on the top of the black box.

WRITER - SHOLLY FISCH   PENCILLER - ROBERT POPE   INKER - SCOTT McRAE
COLORIST - HEROIC AGE   LETTERER - MIKE SELLERS   EDITOR - MICHAEL SIGLAIN

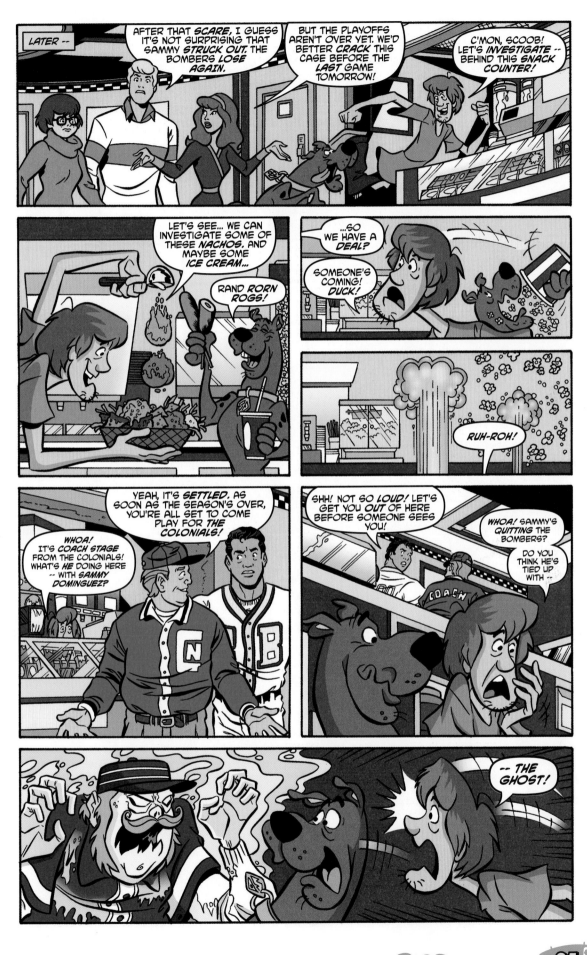

CONTINUED ON PAGE 24

21

GROOVY GAMES!

Spell it out!

Solve each clue and the shaded boxes will reveal the snack that Scooby-Doo is dreaming of!

1. Daphne's last name
2. The gang follow these to solve a mystery
3. The kind of villain Redbeard is
4. The colour of Velma's jumper
5. The spookiest night of the year
6. The ------- Machine

What is it?

Fred can't get a good signal on his Monstervision Tracker. Can you work out what he is looking at?

A

B

C

D

SO SPORTY!

Unscramble each hobby and then follow the maze to find out which member of the gang loves each activity!

ASLEBALB

ESTNIN

SGWINIMM

CGDNINA

FTBLAOOL

SD mini toon

RUH-OH!

NO NEED TO BE AFRAID, OL' PAL. IT'S, LIKE, JUST SOMEONE IN A CUTE EASTER BUNNY COSTUME, SEE?

GRRRR!

RIKES!

ZOINKS! RUN, SCOOBS!

Dear Shaggy

Shaggy uses his immense brain power and knowledge of all things groovy to help the people of Coolsville solve their problems!

Dear Shaggy,

It's my sister's Birthday next week and I don't know what to get her. Any cool ideas?

Thanks, Engelbert Galumpton

Hey there Engelbert! Like, it's totally tricky finding cool gifts for gals. Daphne likes anything purple and fluffy, so maybe some purple fluff would be good? Hee hee! Food is always a winner in my world, so howzabout a big Birthday cake? That would be awesome!

Dear Shaggy,

There's a ghost in my loo and it's driving me crazy. Every time I need to go, the ghost appears, shouts "Boo!" and I have to run away with my legs crossed which is not easy! What can I do?

Yours desperately,
Mr. Piddle

Like, that is one mean ghost! I suggest you build a new bathroom and leave Mr. Spook to enjoy his own little ghost's room. If that isn't possible, run into the bathroom, shove the ghosty down the loo and pull the chain. That'll teach him!

BOO!

Dear Shaggy,

My friend thinks he's right but I say he's wrong and that I'm right. I said that you write with your right hand but he said I'm wrong and you write with your left hand and not your right. Am I right or wrong?

Yours sincerely, Rita Writer

Zoinks! Like, I have so not got a clue what you are asking me so I'm gonna go for the safe answer and say you are both right! Is that right or wrong? Whoa, totally confused!

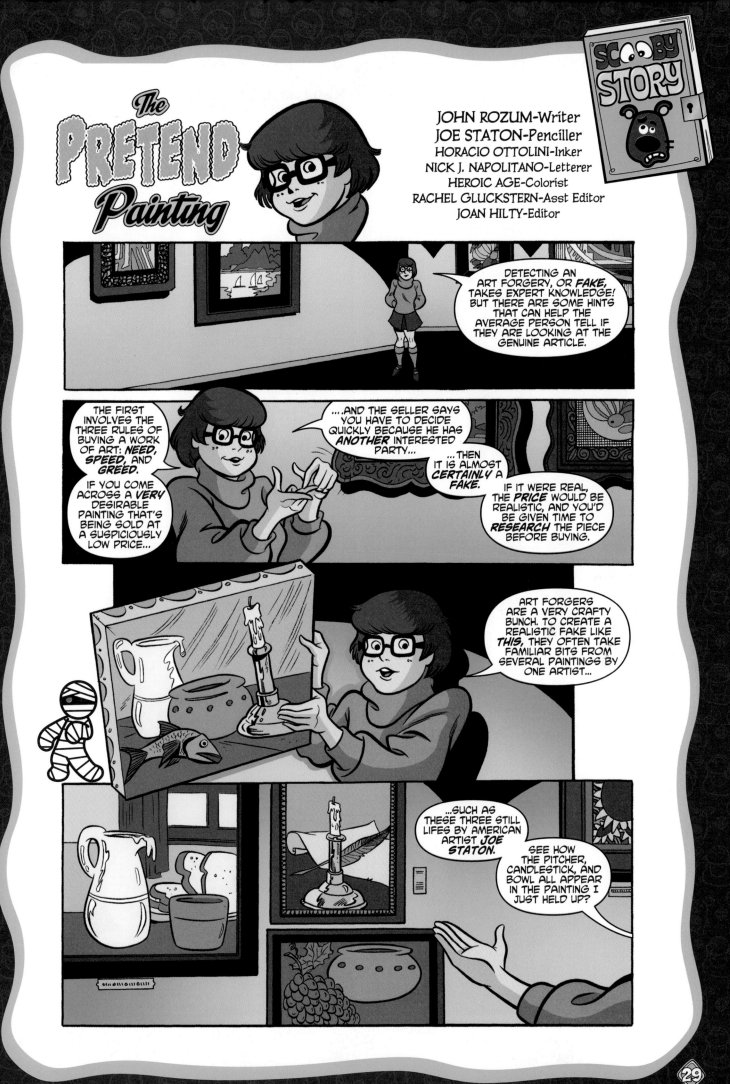

ANOTHER TRICK FORGERS USE IS TO MAKE THEIR PAINTINGS LOOK *OLDER*, BY USING *HEAT* TO ARTIFICIALLY AGE THEM.

THESE TRICKS MAKE THE PAINTING SEEM MORE AUTHENTIC, AND MORE *TEMPTING!*

THERE ARE SCIENTIFIC WAYS TO DETERMINE THE *AGE* OF A PAINTING, BUT THEY *ARE* NOT FOOLPROOF. ART FORGERS KNOW THIS, AND THEY CONCENTRATE ON THE *APPEARANCE* OF THE PAINTING ITSELF.

CAPTURING THE *TECHNIQUE* AND *ENERGY* OF THE *GENUINE* ARTIST IS THE *HARDEST* ASPECT OF A PAINTING TO DUPLICATE!

FORGERS AND CROOKED ART DEALERS OFTEN TRY TO MAKE A FAKE CONVINCING BY TELLING AN ELABORATE STORY ABOUT HOW THE PAINTING CAME INTO THEIR POSSESSION.

THE MORE *COMPLICATED* THE TRAIL OF OWNERSHIP, THE MORE LIKELY THE PAINTING IS A FAKE!

ANOTHER HINT TO UNCOVERING A FAKE IS THAT THEY ARE USUALLY *FASHIONABLE* ONES. IF AN UNKNOWN *PICASSO* SUDDENLY TURNS UP WHEN PICASSO IS *POPULAR,* THEN IT'S PROBABLY FAKE.

FORGERS DON'T FAKE *UNPOPULAR* ARTISTS, FOR THE SAME REASON THAT *COUNTERFEITERS* DON'T PRINT *ONE DOLLAR BILLS*-- IT'S NOT WORTH ENOUGH MONEY TO DO IT!

HAUNTED HIGH SCHOOL!

Think your teachers are scary?
Well at least they're not DEAD scary!
Get ready to tour Hell View High –
the most haunted high school in history!

Dining Hall
Not even Shaggy or Scooby could be hungry enough to eat a bowl of boiled brains dished up by the zombie dinnerladies!

Professor Mummy

Gremlin

Nurse Nightmare

Horrible History Department

EGYPT

HISTORY

SCHOOL NURSE

PRINCIPAL

Ghoul Bus

SCHOOL BUS

HVH

MYSTERY INC.

TERROR TOURS

Tree Demon

Headless Headmaster!
You don't want to mess with the headless headmaster – if he gives you detention you'll be spending it in HELL!

CONTINUED ON PAGE 43

Snack Stop!

The gang are enjoying a snack stop at their favourite diner, The Malt Shop. Can you spot all of the dishes from the menu hidden in the grid?

P	O	T	A	T	O	E	S	Y	K	B	N
I	A	B	P	A	N	L	I	A	I	U	B
Z	I	S	U	B	Y	E	E	W	L	R	U
Z	N	A	T	S	D	T	L	B	O	A	R
A	A	N	S	A	S	E	K	S	C	G	D
G	G	D	W	O	N	A	A	P	C	E	L
R	R	W	N	M	A	K	E	S	O	U	P
C	H	I	C	K	E	N	A	P	R	E	C
R	S	C	A	Y	B	N	I	V	B	C	I
H	I	H	O	T	D	O	G	Y	G	H	P
P	F	T	I	E	S	T	O	R	R	A	C
S	H	A	M	B	U	R	G	E	R	R	S

Salad
Pizza
Broccoli
Pasta
Sandwich
Hot dog
Steak
Soup
Chicken
Beans
Potatoes
Carrots
Fish
Hamburger
Macaroni

There is one dish that isn't in the grid. Can you work out which one it is?

....

The missing word is: Macaroni

GROOVY GAMES!

Dotty Daphne!

Join the dots to discover what Daphne is up to.

1
•35
•34
2
•33
•32
3
•31
4
•30
5
•29
6
•28
7
•27
8   25   •26
9   •24
11   10   •23
12
•22
13
•21
14   20
15   19
16   17   18

DIG THEM BONES!

Match each skeleton with its twin. One doesn't have a matching pair, which one is it?

A
B
C
D
E
F
G

COUNT CONUNDRUM!

Dracula has made **10** creepy changes to this photo of the gang! Can you spot them all?

Tick each time you spot a change! ✓

ANSWER: 1. Bat, 2. Dracula's face, 3. Fred's cape, 4. Blood, 5. Moon, 6. Bat Emblem, 7. Daphne's eyes, 8. Shaggy's hair, 9. Velma's fangs, 10. Scooby's bolts.

CONTINUED FROM PAGE 38

SCOOBY WHO?

Two members of Mystery Inc. are hiding amongst all these lines.
Shade each shape with a dot inside to find out who!

48

CONTINUED ON PAGE 55

53

CREEPY COLOUR!

Grab your colouring
pens and go colour crazy
on this scary scene!

54

CONTINUED FROM PAGE 53

THE NEXT DAY, AS *DARKNESS* AGAIN FALLS ACROSS VLADSBURG...

I...I DON'T *BELIEVE* IT--!

HOW COULD THIS *HAPPEN?*

CITY · HALL

LIKE, SHOULDN'T WE *CALL* SOMEONE?

WHO'S *LEFT* TO CALL? IT LOOKS LIKE EVERYBODY'S ALREADY HERE!

IT WAS OUR *DUTY* TO SEND OUT A *WARNING* ABOUT THE BARON. I GUESS *SOME* REPORTERS THOUGHT IT WAS WORTH A *STORY.*

NOW, *THAT'S* OL' DOC RIPLEY! *HE* WAS A YOUNG DOCTOR IN TOWN THE *FIRST* TIME THE BARON WAS AROUND...

...THE *FANG MARKS* WERE MADE BY THE *SAME* MAN, WHO THEN PROCEEDED TO *DRAIN* MUCH OF THEIR BLOOD.

DOC, THIS IS ONE OF THE YOUNGSTERS *SAVED* MY LIFE LAST NIGHT.

HARD TO BELIEVE THAT BLOOD-SUCKING MONSTER IS *BACK!*

YES, SIR. BUT AT LEAST *THIS* TIME, THE BARON HASN'T *KILLED* ANYONE.

YET! THAT *FIEND* NEARLY *RUINED* VLADSBURG ONCE...!

NEWS 4

TRUE...BUT THEN FOR YEARS *AFTER,* IT BROUGHT A LOT OF *TOURISTS* TO TOWN, LIKE PEOPLE GO TO SALEM, MASSACHUSETTS BECAUSE OF ITS HISTORY OF THE *WITCH TRIALS.*

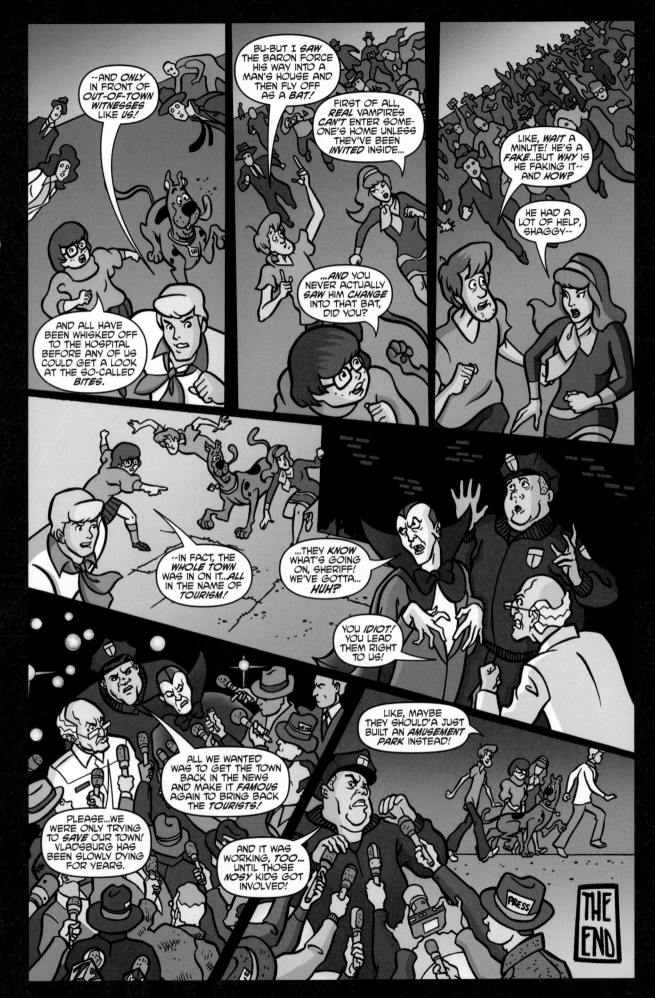

Velma's Detective Test!

Were you being a good detective during Mystery Inc.'s latest adventure? Take this test to find out!

Tick the correct answers! ✓

1 What was the town REALLY called?

YOU ARE NOW ENTERING
HELLSVILLE, PA
"Baron Aderlass Bit Here"
A

YOU ARE NOW ENTERING
VLADSBURG, PA
"Baron Aderlass Bit Here"
B

YOU ARE NOW ENTERING
DRAKOV, PA
"Baron Aderlass Bit Here"
C

2 Can you find one thing we've changed about the vampire?

A Teeth
B Ears
C Bow Tie

3 What were Scoob and Shaggy afraid of here?

A
B
C